BRYAN LEE O'MALLEY'S

edited by James Lucas Jones | design by Bryan Lee O'Malley & Keith Wood

Published by Fourth Estate

First published in 2004 in the United States by Oni Press.

First published in Great Britain in 2010 by
Fourth Estate
An imprint of HarperCollins*Publishers*
77–85 Fulham Palace Road
London W6 8JB
www.4thestate.co.uk

1

ISBN: 978-0-00-739856-0

Printed in Great Britain by Clays Ltd, St Ives plc

special thanks to
  Hope Larson
  Christopher Butcher
  Carla, Amanda, Catriona & Lynette
  James Lucas Jones
  AND YOU.

JUST SO I TELL YOU BEFORE YOU HEAR SOME DIRTY LIES FROM SOMEONE ELSE, YES, I'M DATING A 17-YEAR-OLD.

WALLACE WELLS
ROOMMATE
25 YEARS OLD
RATING: 7.5/10

IS HE CUTE?

HA, HA, HA, HA, HA.

I / can't be sure / but I think I heard you / crawl thru the door / you / didn't say a word / and i think you tried to go to bed / but instead you went to floor / you've been out drinking with the other boys again / telling them no we are only friends

Hey Kids! Now you can play along with Sex Bob-omb at home! It's easy, because they're kind of crappy! Look, this whole song only uses 3 chords!

G   C   Em

4/4 rock, fast, hard, sloppy

end / and where do you begin? / you've been out partying with guys i've never met / drinking beer and smoking cigarettes / killing brain cells and killing me / oh stop pretending / that this isn't really ending / and I will stop resenting you

4

RAMONA COME CLOSER

NICE ONE, SCOTT!
NOW TURN THE PAGE.

SO WHO'S THE NEW GUY?

IT'S A... GIRL.

THEY GOT A GIRL DRUMMER??

SHE'S THEIR SECRET WEAPON! THEY CALL HER TRASHA, AND SHE'S EIGHT YEARS OLD.

I HEAR THEY DISCOVERED HER AT THE PACIFIC MALL ARCADE, PLAYING *DRUM-MANIA*. SHE HAS SO MUCH A.D.D., IT'S NOT EVEN FUNNY.

"TRASHA"
AKA TRISHA HA, AGE 8

I HATE HER *SO* MUCH.

WELL, LET'S DO IT! LET'S PRACTICE! WE'VE GOT 24 HOURS!

24 HRS

LATER

GIRLZ

UM... ARE YOU RELATED TO SCOTT?

SCOTT PILGRIM? I'M HIS SISTER!

OH, COOL... I'M RAMONA.

I'M STACEY. NICE TO MEET YOU!

SO HOW DO YOU KNOW SCOTT?

HE'S... UM, HE'S A FRIEND.

UPSET PEOPLE ROCK

MATTHEW PATEL WAS THE ONLY NON-WHITE, NON-JOCK KID IN SCHOOL. PROBABLY THE ONLY ONE FOR MILES AROUND, OR IN THE ENTIRE STATE, FOR ALL I KNOW. SO, OF COURSE...

WE JOINED FORCES AND TOOK 'EM ALL OUT. WE WERE ONE HELL OF A TEAM. NOTHING COULD BEAT MATTHEW'S MYSTICAL POWERS COMBINED WITH MY BRUTE STRENGTH.

NOTHING BUT PRE-ADOLESCENT CAPRICIOUSNESS.

NEXT!

Does Scott & Ramona's burgeoning relationship have a future? Isn't Scott still supposedly dating Knives Chau? Who is Ramona's second evil ex-boyfriend, and why is he in Toronto? Who are The Clash At Demonhead, and what kind of bizarre art-punky music do they play? Who's their hot girl keyboardist, and what's her relation to Scott? Why are they Knives Chau's new favorite band? Fights! Drama! Secrets revealed! The answers to all these questions and more! It's all coming in...

SCOTT PILGRIM VERSUS THE WORLD

BRYAN LEE O'MALLEY

LOVED BY ANIMALS

Illustration of the Author by Corey S. Lewis The Rey

BRYAN LEE O'MALLEY has been alive since 1979. He plays some guitar and keyboards, but is pretty bad at bass. His first book was called **LOST AT SEA**. His second book is this one. You can learn more about him at **WWW.RADIOMARU.COM**